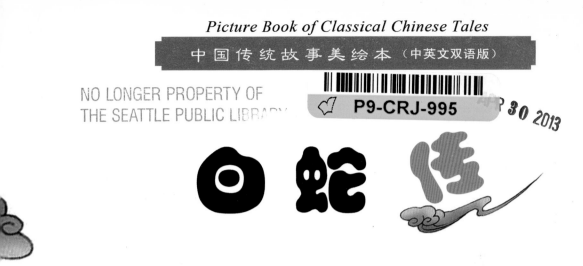

中国传统故事美绘本（中英文双语版）

白蛇传

The Tale of the White Serpent

传说中国南宋年间，阳春三月，两位年轻女子来到了美丽的西子湖畔。年纪稍长的一袭白衣，清雅脱俗，名叫白素贞；一旁陪伴的侍女一袭青衣，眉目清秀，名唤小青。她们是经过千年修炼的白蛇和青蛇，到杭州来寻找多年前救过她们的许仙，报答救命之恩。

　　两人边走边欣赏美景，不觉走到湖边。湖上有一叶小舟，船头站着一位温文尔雅的青年男子。那人正是许仙。白素贞望着眼前的男子，不禁看呆了。

Legends have it that, on a sunny, spring day during the Southern Song Dynasty (1127~1279) in China, two young girls came to the scenic West Lake in Hangzhou, capital of present-day Zhejiang Province. The older one, dressed in pure white and looking extremely refined and elegant, was Bai Suzhen, while the younger, a girl with fine features and dressed in dark green, was her maid, Xiaoqing. In actual fact, the former was a white serpent while the latter was a dark green one. They had reached their present form after being tempered and disciplined for 1,000 years. They had come to the West Lake to look for Xu Xian, a young man who had saved their life years ago, and to repay him for his kindness.

The two girls rambled along, feasting their eyes on the beautiful scenery all round. In no time, they came to the lakeside. Looking ahead, they saw a small boat on the lake. Standing in the bow was a young man—gentle and cultivated. It was Xu Xian. Bai Suzhen stood spellbound at the sight of this young man.

此时，一片乌云飘来，顿时下起了雨。许仙见两位女子衣服都被淋湿了，便请她们上船避雨。交谈中，白素贞得知许仙自幼丧母寄住姐姐家中，尚未娶妻。两人在交谈中相互产生了爱慕之情。

小船行至清波门，白素贞二人准备上岸。许仙见雨还没停，就把伞借给了她们。两人离船上岸，小青回头说道："许相公，我家住箭桥双茶坊巷口，您明日可来取伞？""不论风雨，我准到。"许仙回答。

All of a sudden, black clouds gathered overhead and it began to rain. Seeing the two girls getting soaked in the downpour, Xu invited them to take shelter in his boat. While chatting, Bai Suzhen learned that Xu had lost his parents as a child and was now staying with his elder sister and that he was still single. The two hearts fell in tune with one another as they chatted.

The boat arrived at the Qingbo Gate where Bai Suzhen and her maid had to get ashore. But it was still raining, so Xu lent them his umbrella. Once on shore, Xiaoqing turned back and said, "Mr Xu, we are staying at the entrance of Shuangchafang Lane near the Arrow Bridge. Would you please come and get your umbrella tomorrow?"

"Yes, you may count on it, come rain or shine," Xu replied.

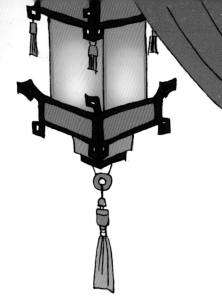

　　第二天，许仙依约来到白宅。白素贞亲自下厨，为他做了一桌丰盛的酒菜。他们边饮酒边聊，互相表明了相知相爱之意。白娘子见许仙清贫无钱办婚事，便命小青拿出银两相送。许仙回到家中禀明姐姐，操办婚事，娶了白素贞为妻。

The following day, Xu Xian came to visit Bai Suzhen. Bai Suzhen did the cooking herself, preparing a tableful of delicacies. Then they chatted over wine and confessed their love to one another. Knowing that Xu was too poor to afford a wedding ceremony, Bai Suzhen told her maid to present Xu with some money. Back home, Xu told his sister the whole story. A wedding ceremony was held and the two tied the knot.

婚后，白素贞与许仙来到镇江，开了一家名叫保安堂的药铺。夫妻俩行医治病，积德行善，治好了许多疑难杂症，而且救治穷人不收分文。周边的人们都跑来找他们看病，附近金山寺的香火反而变得冷清起来。大家都很喜欢善良的白素贞，亲切地称她为"白娘子"。

After their marriage, Bai Suzhen and Xu Xian came to Zhenjiang and started a drug store called Bao'antang (Health Promoting House). They practiced medicine and tried their best to help the ordinary people. They cured lots of people suffering from intractable diseases and even offered free treatment to patients who were poverty-stricken. Instead of going to the Gold Mountain Temple nearby to pray for divine help, people would pour in from near and far to seek practical help from this kind-hearted couple. As a mark of their love for her, people came to call Bai Suzhen "Madam Bai."

一日，许仙外出游玩，遇见一个和尚，自称是金山寺法海长老。法海打量了许仙几眼，把他拉到一边，说："你身上有一股妖气。据我所看，你家中有蛇精作怪。""一派胡言。"许仙不信。"相公，这里有一包雄黄，你回家后放入酒中，叫你夫人喝下，我说的是真是假自有分晓。"法海说着递给他一个药包。

One day, while Xu Xian was out by himself, he ran into a monk. The monk identified himself as Fahai and said he was an elder from the Gold Mountain Temple nearby. He stared at Xu Xian for a while and then took Xu to one side.

"You look so monstrous, young man," Fahai told Xu Xian. "You must be harboring an evil spirit in your home; I can tell."

"Nonsense," Xu objected.

"Well, young man," Fahai persisted, "here is a packet of realgar for you. Mix it into wine when you go home, and ask your wife to drink it. Then you'll know whether I've spoken nonsense or told you the truth."

Fahai handed the pack of realgar to Xu Xian and left.

许仙回家后，依法海之言，哄白娘子喝下药酒。一时间，白娘子只觉得天旋地转，勉强支撑着回房便一头歪倒在床。许仙来看时，只见一条大白蟒横卧在床。惊恐之下，许仙一下子昏死过去。待白娘子醒来，见许仙一点气息也没有了，悲痛得放声大哭。

　　Back at home, Xu Xian coaxed his wife into drinking the wine he had prepared according to Fahai's advice. Immediately, Madam Bai felt as though the world were spinning. She struggled into her room and immediately fell onto her bed.

　　Xu Xian came to see her. To his surprise, a big white serpent was lying in the bed. He fainted dead away. When Madam Bai woke up, she saw Xu Xian lying there lifeless. She burst into tears.

为救许仙性命,白娘子直奔昆仑山。在那里,她拼尽全身力气,盗取了可以起死回生的千年灵芝。许仙服下灵芝,慢慢苏醒过来。白娘子将他带到后院,指着树上挂着的一条白蟒说:"相公,这蛇让你受了惊吓。我已经把它杀了。"许仙相信了,日子又恢复了平静。

In order to bring Xu Xian back to life, Madam Bai rushed into the Kunlun Mountains. Using all her cunning, she stole a 1,000-year-old medicinal herb known as lingzhi (*Ganoderma lucidum*), capable of bringing the dying back to life. After taking the herb, Xu Xian gradually came to his senses. Taking him into the backyard and pointing to a white python hanging on a tree, Madam Bai said, "It was this serpent that scared my dear husband to death. I have killed it." Xu Xian was convinced, and their life returned to normal.

　　可是没过多久，许仙竟然失踪了。原来，他被法海骗到金山寺软禁起来了。白娘子得知消息，带着小青，来到金山寺找法海要人。任凭白娘子苦苦哀求，法海拒不放人，还威胁说："大胆蛇精，再不离开，我就对你们不客气了！"

　　白娘子一怒之下，发动大水。一时间狂风急雨，波浪滔天，眼见金山寺就要被淹没了。法海脱下大红袈裟，用尽毕生功力，向上一抛盖住了寺院。江水涨，寺院也随着涨，始终只漫到底部。只是寺院外的生灵早已淹没在洪水之中。

Before long, Xu Xian mysteriously disappeared. It turned out that Fahai had put him under house arrest in the Gold Mountain Temple. Learning the news, Madam Bai came to the temple, in the company of Xiaoqing, to seek her husband's release. For all her petitioning, however, Fahai refused to let Xu Xian go. He even gave Bai and her maid a warning: "Get out of here right away, you monsters, or I will get hard on you!"

Outraged, Madam Bai decided to cause a flood. A violent storm came, and the downpour created a billowing sea in no time. Higher and higher the sea level grew, and deeper and deeper the Gold Mountain Temple sank. Seeing the imminent threat, Fahai took off his bright, red cassock and cast it over the temple, relying upon his superb magical skills. As a result, the temple kept rising with the sea level which never reached any higher than its foundation. Unfortunately, however, all the living things below it were drowned.

　　白蛇和青蛇水漫金山,犯了天条,天兵天将赶来治罪,帮助法海一起大战白娘子。因为怀有身孕怕动了胎气,白娘子不再恋战,离开了金山寺。

　　西湖断桥之上,白娘子和小青巧遇许仙。原来他挂念妻子,乘着混乱从寺中跑出,四处寻找白娘子的下落。夫妻终于重聚。不久,白娘子生下了一个男孩,取名许仕麟。

The flooding of the Gold Mountain Temple by Madam Bai and Xiaoqing violated the law of Heaven. Divine troops were sent to punish them. Joining hands with Fahai, the troops fought a fierce battle against Bai. Pregnant and afraid of harming the fetus, Bai decided to retreat and left the Gold Mountain Temple.

Back by the West Lake, Madam Bai and Xiaoqing ran into Xu Xian once again on a bridge. It turned out that Xu, sorely missing his wife, had been searching everywhere for her. His efforts ended in a happy reunion. Before long, Madam Bai gave birth to a boy. They named him Xu Shilin.

正当一家人沉浸在幸福之中时，法海出现了。他掏出一个金钵，直向白娘子罩去。白娘子产后虚弱，躲闪不及，一下被镇住，现出了原形。法海将白娘子装入钵中，镇在雷峰塔下。许仙一家，夫妻分散，母子分离，十分凄惨。白娘子和许仙之子许仕麟一天天长大，时常思念母亲。

Just as they were
once again enjoying a
happy family life togeth-
er, Fahai turned up.
Holding a gold bowl, he ran straight to Madam Bai and
cast it down over her. Still too weak from the childbirth
to run away, she got trapped under the bowl and re-
vealed her true form as a snake. Using the gold bowl as
a container, Fahai buried her under Leifeng
Pagoda to prevent her from coming out once
again. The family was broken. Xu Xian lost
his wife, and Xu Shilin, their son, grew up
without a mother.

这一年，许仕麟才学出众考中了状元。他在雷峰塔前祭拜母亲时，遇见了小青。经过数十年修炼，小青功力大增。她大战法海，推倒雷峰塔，救出了白娘子。从此许仙一家人幸福地生活在一起。

法海无处可逃，最后只好躲进螃蟹壳里，再也不敢出来了。

Talented and diligent, Xu Shilin came first in the highest imperial exam one year. When he came to Leifeng Pagoda for a memorial ceremony for his mother, he met with Xiaoqing. Now extremely powerful after scores of years of hard training, Xiaoqing fought a brave battle against Fahai, brought down Leifeng Pagoda, and saved Madam Bai. From then on, Xu Xian and his family lived in happiness.

With no other way to flee from the fight with Xiaoqing, Fahai hid himself in the crab's shell and never dared to show up any more.

完

End